D0636486

Kids IQ
Interactive
Puzzles

Managing Editors: Simon Melhuish and Sarah Wells
Series Editor: Nikole G Bamford
Designer/Illustrator: Linley J Clode
Writer: Philip Carter

Published by
The Lagoon Group
PO Box 311, KT2 5QW, UK
PO Box 990676, Boston, MA 02199, USA

ISBN: 1904797032

www.thelagoongroup.com

Printed in China

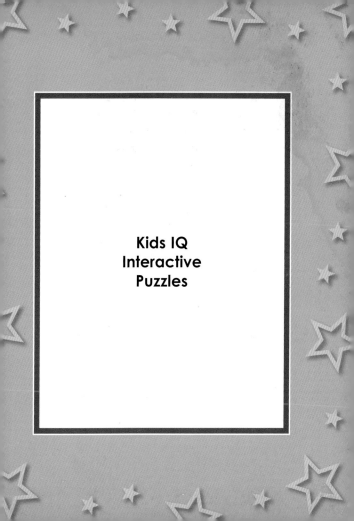

Kids IQ
Interactive
Puzzles

IntelliQuest

UNIQUE BOOK CODE	003

Instructions

First of all make sure you have a Quizmo —

Find the book's unique code (this appears at the top of this page). Use the < and > buttons to scroll to this number on the Quizmo screen. Press the ⏎ button to enter the code, and you're ready to go.

Use the < > scroll buttons to select the question number you want to answer. Press the A, B, C, or D button to enter your chosen answer.

If you are correct the green light beside the button you pressed will flash. You can then use the scroll button to move on to another question.

If your answer is incorrect, the red light beside the button you pressed will flash.

Don't worry, you can try again and again until you have the correct answer, OR move on to another question. (Beware: the more times you guess incorrectly, the lower your final percentage score will be!)

You can finish the quiz at any point — just press the ⬥ button to find out your score and rank as follows:

75% or above	Wow! You're a genius!
50% — 74%	You're one bright spark!
25% — 49%	Oh dear, time to fill up your think tank…
Less than 25%	Emergency! You've got a serious case of brain drain!

If you do press the ⬥ button to find out your score, this will end your session and you will have to use the ⬥ to start again!

HAVE FUN!

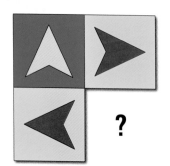

?

A

B

C

D

Which is the missing tile?

WRITE is to **LETTER**

as **PAINT** is to **?**

A **PICTURE**

B **POT**

C **BRUSH**

D **WET**

6, 12, 18, 24, 30, 36, ?, 48

A	B
38	40

C	D
42	44

What number is missing?

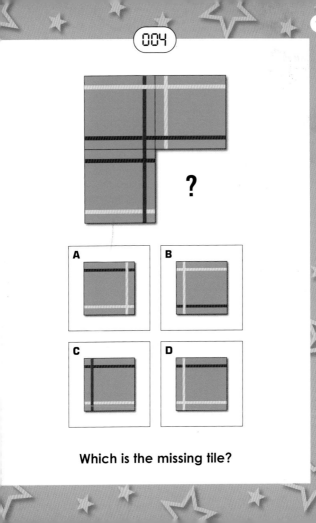

Which is the missing tile?

A	they are stable in rough seas

B	they can be anchored in the harbour

C	they can be steered

D	they will not sink

Ships have rudders so that...?

2 4 8 1 4 3
7 2 9 5 8 2

A

59731

B

59371

C

95731

D

97513

Which is a list of all the odd numbers
in reverse from the above list?

A

B

C

D

What comes next?

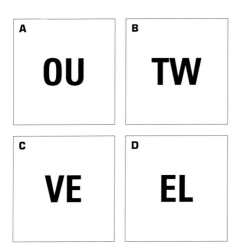

A OU

B TW

C VE

D EL

Three of the four pieces above
can be combined to spell out the name
of a number between ten and fifteen.
Which is the odd one out?

A 4

B 12

C 8

D 16

If you slice a pizza from side to side four times so that each cut goes through the middle, how many pieces will you have?

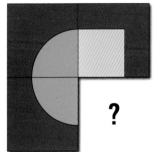

?

A

B

C

D

Which is the missing tile?

A. old

B. elderly

C. new

D. aged

Which is the odd one out?

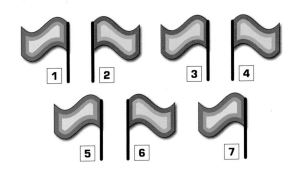

Which is the odd one out?

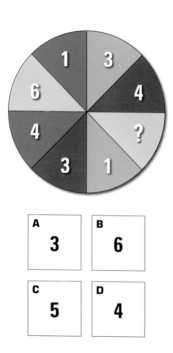

A 3

B 6

C 5

D 4

What number should replace
the question mark?

A

B

C

D

Which is the missing tile?

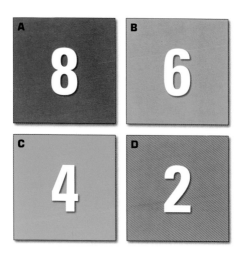

Sally is 9 years old and Harry is 16 years old. How many years ago was Harry twice as old as Sally?

014

A new

B solid

C safe

D wide

Which word means the opposite of DANGEROUS?

5 (20) 4

3 (24) 8

7 (?) 2

A	B
16	28

C	D
14	12

**What number should replace
the question mark?**

016

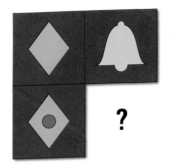

?

A

B

C

D

Which is the missing tile?

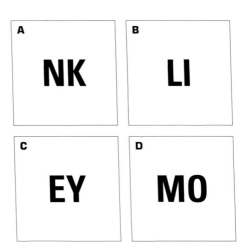

A NK

B LI

C EY

D MO

Three of the four pieces above can be combined to spell out the name of an animal. Which is the odd one out?

41 11 37 22
14 48 16

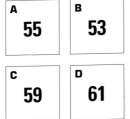

A	B
55	53

C	D
59	61

Add the lowest number in the above list to
the largest number. What is the total?

A

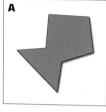

B

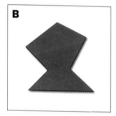

C

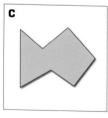

D

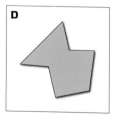

Which piece is identical in shape to the piece above?

5, 12, 19, 26, ?

A 34	**B** 32
C 31	**D** 33

What number comes next?

A beach

B vacation

C sunshine

D pray

Which word means the same as HOLIDAY?

A top

B grass

C sheep

D bricks

Which of the above does a
HILL always have?

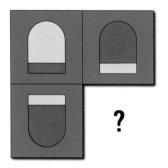

?

A

B

C

D

Which is the missing tile?

A

UR

B

CH

C

BI

D

CH

Three of the four pieces above
can be combined to spell out
the name of a religious building?
Which is the odd one out?

123, ?, 345, 456, 567

A 234	**B** 146
C 256	**D** 246

What number is missing?

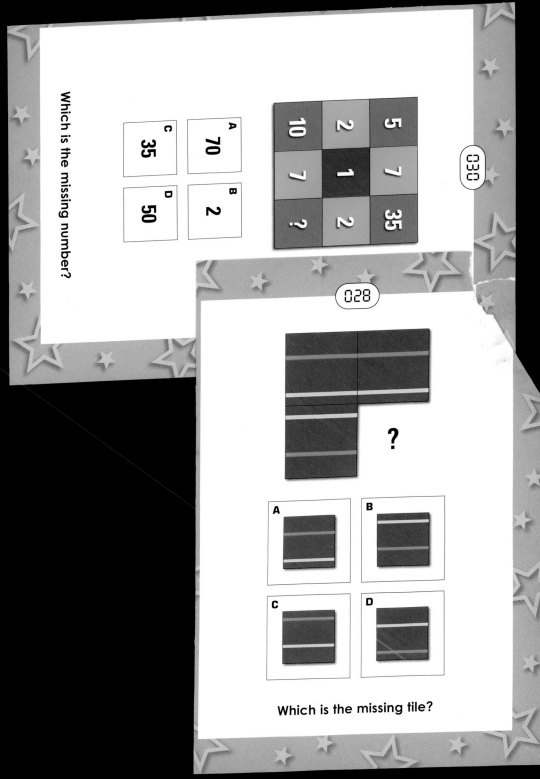

Which is the missing number?

A 70	**B** 2
C 35	**D** 50

?

A	**B**
C	**D**

Which is the missing tile?

Which is the missing tile?

A William

B Karen

C Anne

D Joan

Who is the odd one out?

A **end**

B **give**

C **extend**

D **leave**

Which word means the opposite of BEGIN?

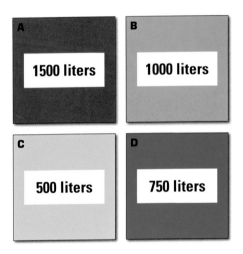

A 1500 liters

B 1000 liters

C 500 liters

D 750 liters

A water fountain sprays out water
at the rate of 3000 liters per hour.
How much water would be sprayed out
between the times of 12.25 and 12.40?

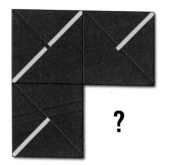

?

A

B

C

D

Which is the missing file?

A **roof**

B **shed**

C **building**

D **cover**

Which word means the same as HUT?

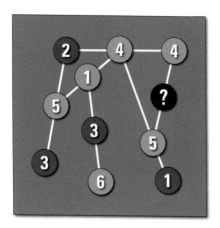

A
3

B
2

C
1

D
4

Which number should go in the
empty circle?

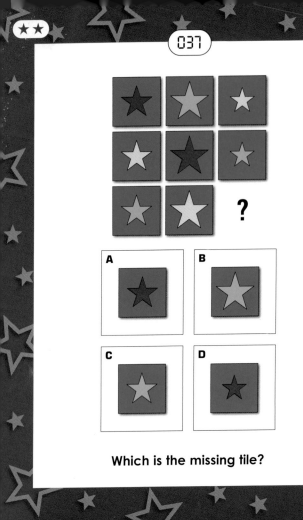

Which is the missing tile?

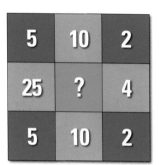

5	10	2
25	?	4
5	10	2

A 10

B 20

C 50

D 100

Which number should replace
the question mark?

Which of these anagrams,
when unscrambled, is NOT
something you would wear?

A
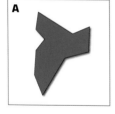

B
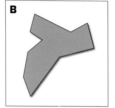

C
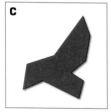

D

Which piece is identical
in shape to the piece above?

A 6

B 7

C 8

D 9

What number should replace
the question mark?

ANKLE is to **FOOT**

as **WRIST** is to **?**

A **ARM**

B **LEG**

C **HAND**

D **FINGER**

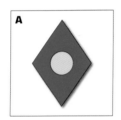

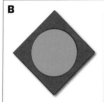

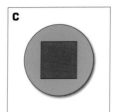

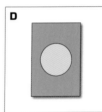

Which is the odd one out?

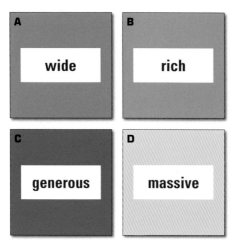

A wide

B rich

C generous

D massive

Which word means the opposite of SMALL?

0, 1, 3, 6, 10, 15, ?

A 22

B 21

C 20

D 19

What comes next?

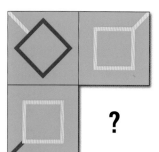

?

A

B

C

D

Which is the missing tile?

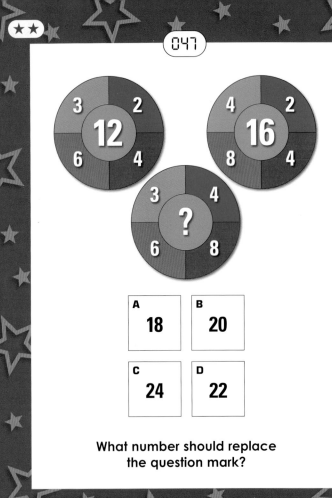

A 18

B 20

C 24

D 22

What number should replace
the question mark?

A **class**

B **master**

C **know**

D **educate**

Which word means the same as TEACH?

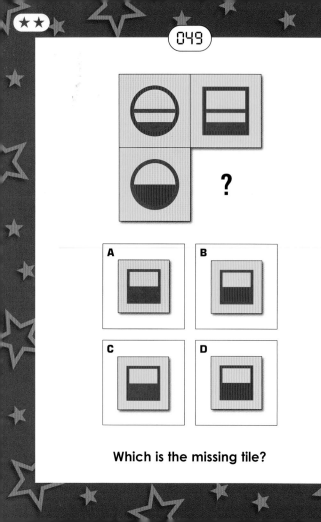

049

A

B

C

D

Which is the missing tile?

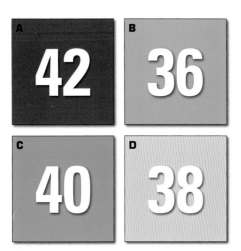

A 42

B 36

C 40

D 38

Five lions and seven ostriches together
have 34 feet. How many feet
have seven lions and five ostriches?

A **mistake**

B **change**

C **punish**

D **destroy**

Which word means the same as ERROR?

A 10

B 11

C 12

D 13

How many lines appear above?

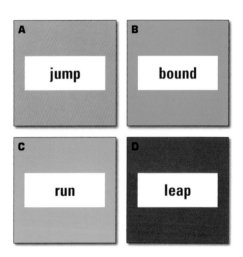

A jump

B bound

C run

D leap

Which is the odd one out?

1, 4, 4, 8, 7, 11, ?

A 9

B 10

C 11

D 12

What comes next?

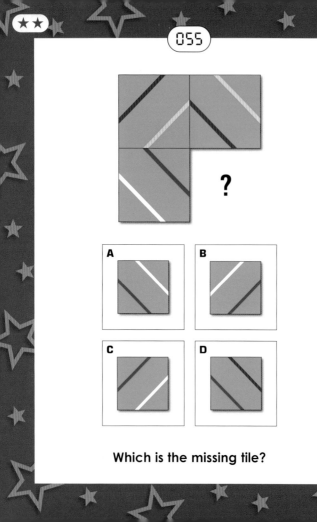

A

B

C

D

Which is the missing tile?

100, 91, 82, 73, 64, 55, 46, ?

A 37

B 35

C 39

D 34

What comes next?

A **election**

B **cross**

C **ballot**

D **leader**

A ——————— is a secret method of voting. What word is missing?

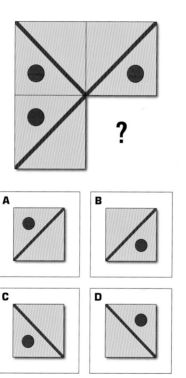

A

B

C

D

Which is the missing tile?

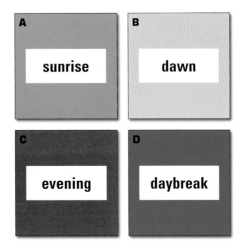

A sunrise

B dawn

C evening

D daybreak

Which is the odd one out?

1, 11, 20, 28, 35, ?

A 39

B 40

C 41

D 42

What comes next?

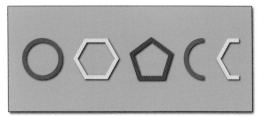

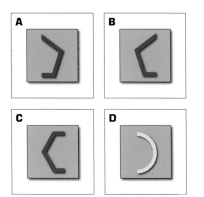

What comes next?

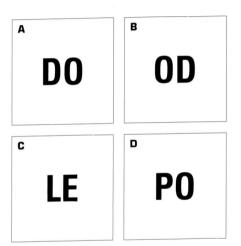

A **DO**

B **OD**

C **LE**

D **PO**

Three of the four pieces can be
combined to spell out the name of a type
of dog. Which is the odd one out?

A 3

B 2

C 1

D 0

Which is the missing number?

A 38

B 34

C 48

D 52

Which number in the circle is double one of the numbers in the square?

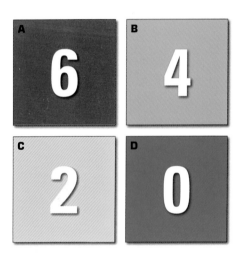

How many of each animal did Moses take in the Ark?

3, 6, 12, 24, 48, ?

A
86

B
90

C
94

D
96

What comes next?

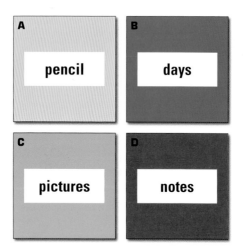

A pencil

B days

C pictures

D notes

Which of the above does a
calendar always have?

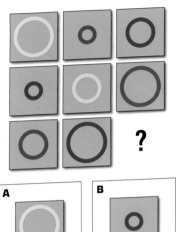

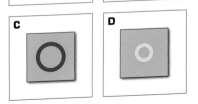

Which is the missing tile?

A **stork**

B **tiger**

C **monkey**

D **leopard**

Which is the odd one out?

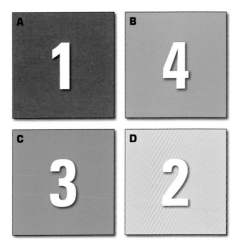

A 1

B 4

C 3

D 2

Divide 12 between Dave, Jean and Kate and give Dave 2 more than Jean, and Jean 2 more than Kate. How many does Jean get?

?

A

B

C

D

Which is the missing tile?

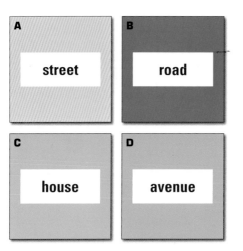

A street

B road

C house

D avenue

Which is the odd one out?

12, 10, 7, 3, ?

A	B
-2	0

C	D
-1	1

What comes next?

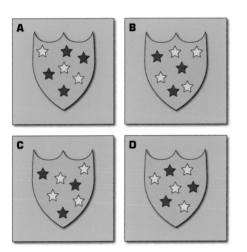

Which is the odd one out?

A empty

B quick

C departed

D dry

Which word means the same as GONE?

★★★

17 (51) 3

19 (38) ?

A
4

B
3

C
2

D
5

What number should replace
the question mark?

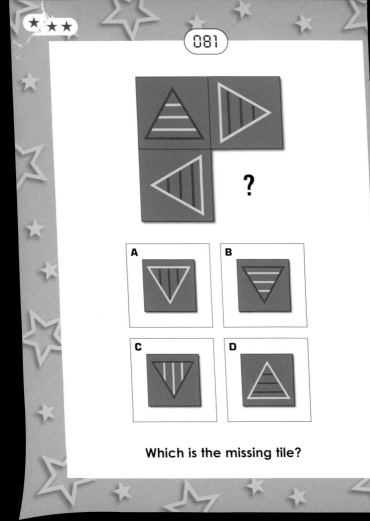

Which is the missing tile?

13, 26, 39, ?, 65

A 63	**B** 52
C 54	**D** 53

Which number is missing?

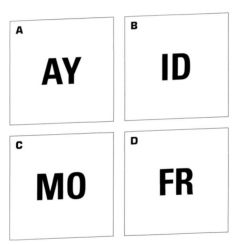

A AY

B ID

C MO

D FR

Three of the four pieces can be combined to spell out the name of a day of the week. Which is the odd one out?

★★★

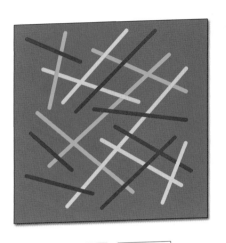

A	B
14	17

C	D
16	18

How many lines appear above?

★★★

A	onward lend

B	worn landed

C	and old wren

D	new lord den

**Which of the above is not
an anagram of WONDERLAND?**

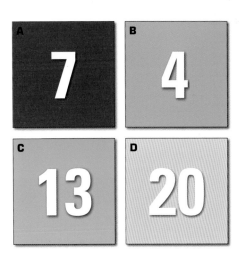

In a drawer are 10 pairs of identical red socks, 3 pairs of identical blue socks and 6 pairs of identical brown socks. If it were pitch black dark, how many socks would you need to take out of the drawer to make sure you had an identical pair?

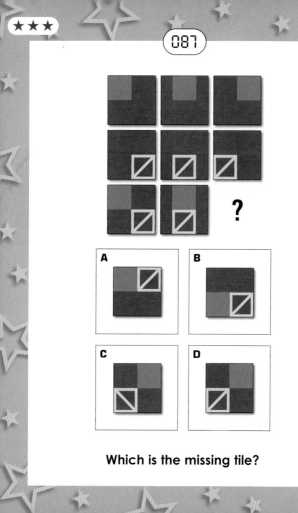

Which is the missing tile?

Which is the odd one out?

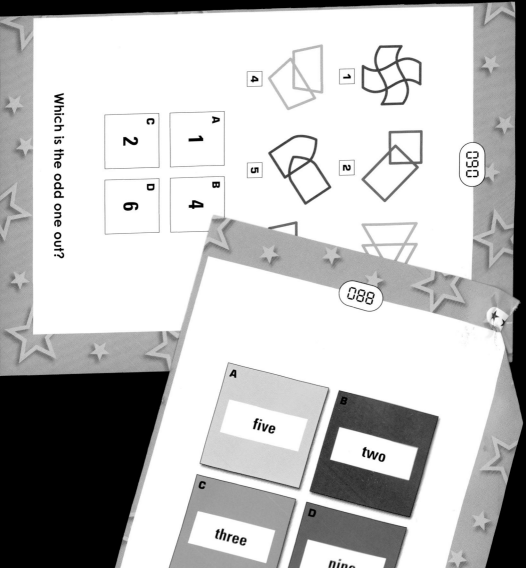

4

1

5

2

A 1
B 4
C 2
D 6

A five

B two

C three

D nine

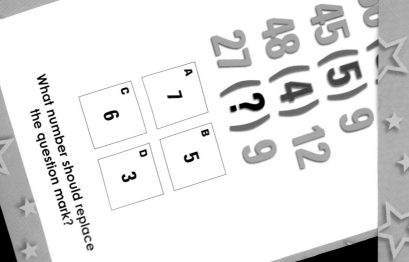

What number should replace the question mark?

A 7	**B** 5
C 6	**D** 3

45 (5) 9
48 (4) 12
27 (?) 9

A **holiday**

B **road**

C **map**

D **trip**

Which word means the same as JOURNEY?

28 (20) 12
7 (6) 5
10 (13) 16
9 (?) 17

A	B
13	7

C	D
8	11

Which number should replace
the question mark?

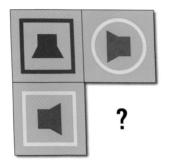

?

A

B

C

D

Which is the missing tile?

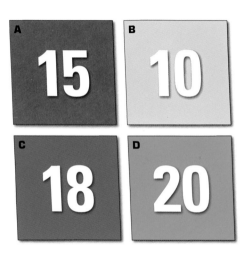

A 15

B 10

C 18

D 20

How many minutes is it before midnight
if one hour later it will be three
times as many minutes past midnight?

A **change**

B **build**

C **improve**

D **damage**

Which word means the opposite of SPOIL?

A **42**

B **3**

C **39**

D

What is 75% of 52?

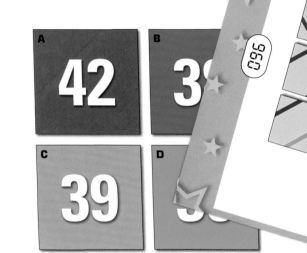

?

B

A

D

C

Which is the missing tile?

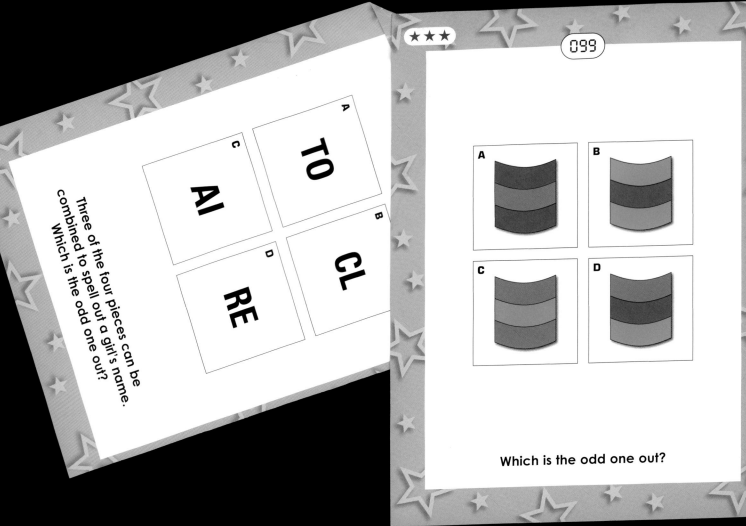

Three of the four pieces can be combined to spell out a girl's name. Which is the odd one out?

A   TO
B   CL
C   AI
D   RE

★★★   099

A   B
C   D

Which is the odd one out?

A calm

B windy

C frosty

D wet

Which word means the opposite of HOT?

100, 99, 97, 94, 90, 85, 79, 72, ?

A 64

B 62

C 61

D 66

What comes next?

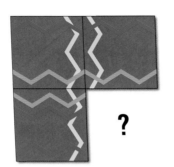

?

A

B

C

D

Which is the missing tile?

A catches hair

B crease hitch

C hectic share

D teaches rich

Which of the above is not
an anagram of CHESHIRE CAT?

| | 9 | 13 | 17 | 21 |
| 18 | 26 | 34 | ? |

A 38

B 40

C 42

D 84

Which number should replace
the question mark?

How many circles appear above?

★★★

EYE is to **SIGHT**

as **TONGUE** is to **?**

A **SPEECH**

B **LIPS**

C **TASTE**

D **LICK**

1, 16, 31, 46, ?

A 59

B 61

C 63

D 65

What number comes next?

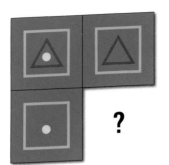

?

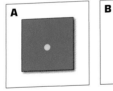

A

B

C

D

Which is the missing tile?

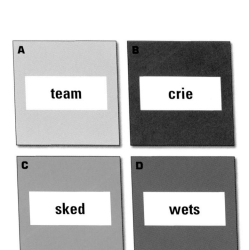

A team

B crie

C sked

D wets

Which of these anagrams,
when unscrambled, is
NOT something you would eat?

Monday 32°

Tuesday 34°

Wednesday 30°

A 30°

B 34°

C 32°

D 35°

The above are the temperatures for a region for three days. What is the average temperature over the three days?

A 1

B 2

C 3

D 4

If a different digit is placed in each square so that each row, column and long diagonal adds up to 15, which digit will be in the bottom right-hand corner?

A The couples were married in a leap year

B The couples were married on a cruise

C The couples were married in different years but the Whites separated for a while

D The couples were married at midnight

Mr and Mrs Black are due to celebrate their silver wedding anniversary one day before their friends, Mr and Mrs White. No-one will believe the Whites were married first, but they were. How can this be?

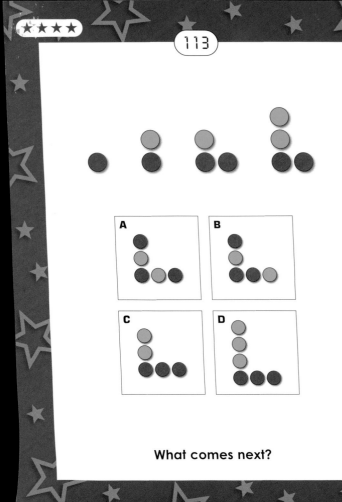

What comes next?

1, 10, 2, 9,
3, 8, 4, ?

A 7

B 5

C 6

D 1

What comes next?

A **animals**

B **grass**

C **rocks**

D **trees**

Rubber is obtained from —————.
What word is missing?

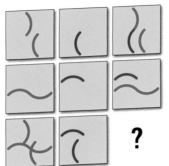

?

A

B

C

D

Which is the missing tile?

A

AR

B

EV

C

EN

D

ST

Three of the four pieces can be
combined to spell out a boy's name.
Which is the odd one out?

1.5, 2.75, 4, 5.25, ?

What comes next?

A 7.5

B 6.25

C 7.25

D 6.5

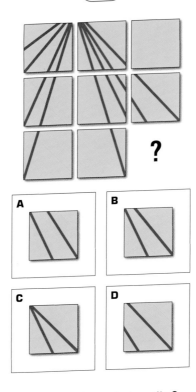

Which is the missing tile?

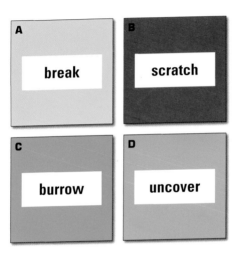

A break

B scratch

C burrow

D uncover

Which word means the same as DIG?

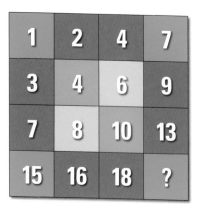

A 23

B 19

C 21

D 25

What number should replace
the question mark?

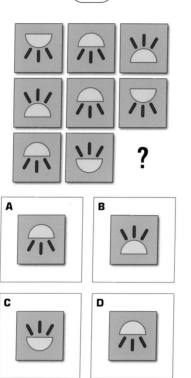

Which is the missing tile?

THEN is to **NOW**

as **PAST** is to **?**

A SOMETIME

B PRESENT

C FUTURE

D NEVER

<table>
<tr><td>A
8</td><td>B
6</td></tr>
<tr><td>C
9</td><td>D
10</td></tr>
</table>

How many triangles of different shapes and sizes can you find in the figure above?

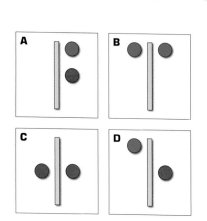

What comes next?

A

TE

B

NU

C

MI

D

TI

Three of the four pieces can be
combined to spell out a unit of time.
Which is the odd one out?

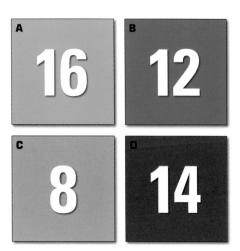

A 16

B 12

C 8

D 14

Tom has twice as many sweets as Dick and
Dick has twice as many as Harry.
Altogether they have 56.
How many sweets has Dick?

A

B

C

D

What comes next?

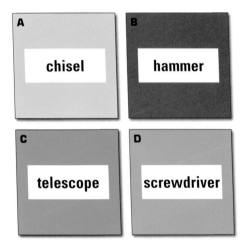

A chisel

B hammer

C telescope

D screwdriver

Which is the odd one out?

★★★★

100, 92.5, 85, 77.5, 70, ?

A 64

B 62.5

C 61.5

D 63.5

What comes next?

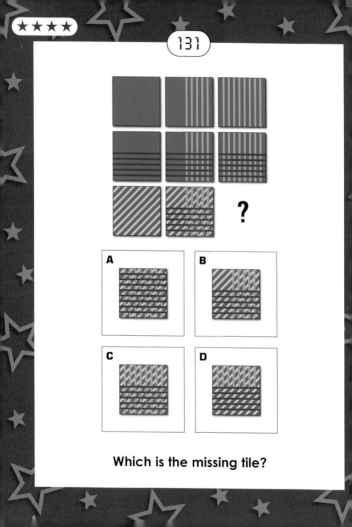

A

B

C

D

Which is the missing tile?

A chase

B escape

C flee

D bolt

Which word means both a
fastener and to run off?

A	B
6	2

C	D
10	7

What number is missing?

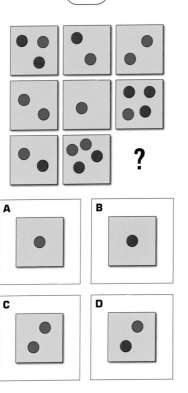

Which is the missing tile?

A mlpu

B perag

C toga

D palpe

Which of these anagrams,
when unscrambled, is not something
you would put in a fruit bowl?

A 0.6

B 0.7

C 0.75

D 0.8

What is the decimal value of 35% plus 45%?

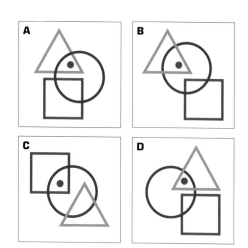

Which is the odd one out?

A It is colder

B It contains oil

C It contains salt

D It contains millions of tiny sea creatures

Why is sea water heavier
than fresh water?

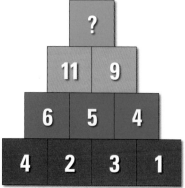

A
18

B
16

C
24

D
20

What number should replace
the question mark?

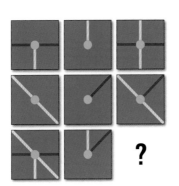

?

A

B

C

D

Which is the missing tile?

A wire bath bit

B with rate rib

C with bear bit

D tear with bib

Which of the following is
NOT an anagram of WHITE RABBIT?

0.3, 0.45, 0.6, 0.75, 0.9, ?

A 1.15

B 1.5

C 1.05

D 1.1

What comes next?

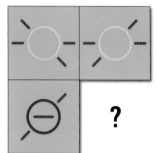

?

A

B

C

D

Which is the missing tile?

A **eye**

B **foot**

C **ear**

D **nose**

Which is the odd one out?

A 19

B 15

C 18

D 17

What number is missing?

★ ★ ★ ★

?

A

B

C

D

Which is the missing tile?

A

GU

B

AU

C

ER

D

ST

Three of the four pieces can be
combined to spell out a month of the year.
Which is the odd one out?

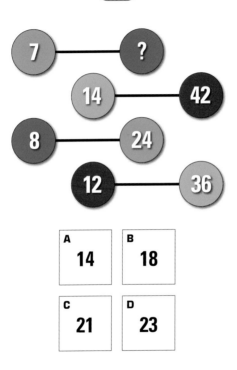

A
14

B
18

C
21

D
23

What number should replace
the question mark?

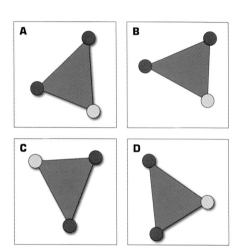

Which is the odd one out?

VENUS is to **PLANET**

as **SUN** is to **?**

A EARTH

B STAR

C SOLAR

D MOON

1, 3, 4, 7, 11, 18, ?

A	B
29	26

C	D
27	25

What comes next?

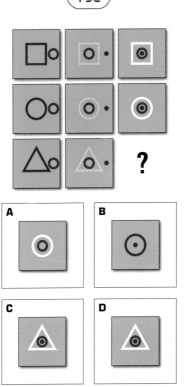

A

B

C

D

Which is the missing tile?

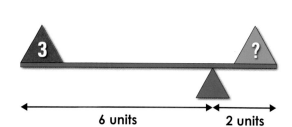

6 units   2 units

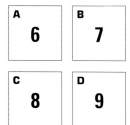

A
6

B
7

C
8

D
9

What weight should replace the question
mark in order for the scale to balance?

A quote fans here

B oh! frequent sea

C often he equals

D square then foe

**Which of the above is not
an anagram of QUEEN OF HEARTS?**

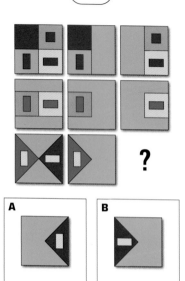

Which is the missing tile?

SAND is to **DESERT**

as **WATER** is to **?**

A LAND

B OCEAN

C SHIP

D FISH

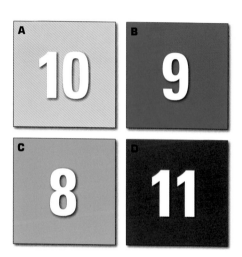

A 10

B 9

C 8

D 11

Alice had twice as many sweets as George. She then ate one sweet and gave George 3, which meant they now each had the same number. How many was that?

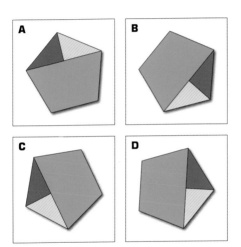

A

B

C

D

Which is the odd one out?

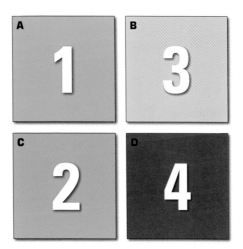

If I had 30% of 70 how many more
would I need to have 40% of 60?

A

GE

B

AN

C

CE

D

FR

Three of the four pieces can be
combined to spell out a country in Europe.
Which is the odd one out?

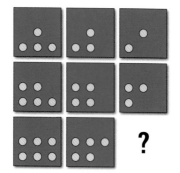

?

A

B

C

D

Which is the missing tile?

★★★★★

A **kitchen**

B **attic**

C **bedroom**

D **garden**

Which is the odd one out?

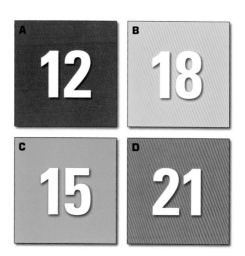

A 12	**B** 18
C 15	**D** 21

Originally Edward had three times as many as William, and Amy did not have any. But then Edward gave three to William and four to Amy, which meant that Edward and William now had the same and each had twice as many as Amy. How many did Edward have originally?

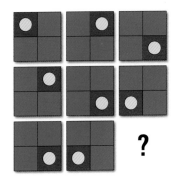

?

A

B

C

D

Which is the missing tile?

A **crook**

B **believe**

C **person**

D **article**

Which word means the same as THING?

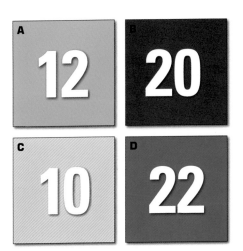

A 12

B 20

C 10

D 22

How many minutes is it before
12 noon if one hour ago it was twice
as many minutes past 10 am?

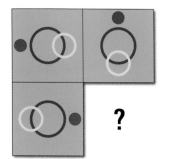

?

A

B
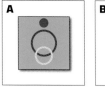

C

D

Which is the missing tile?

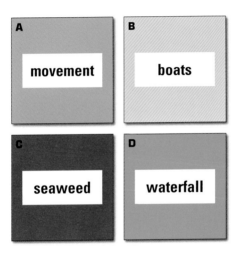

A movement

B boats

C seaweed

D waterfall

Which of the above does a
river always have?

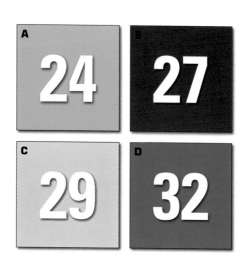

Tom has three times as many
as Dick. Between them they have 36.
How many has Tom?

★★★★★

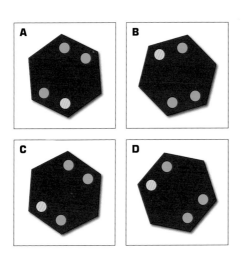

Which is the odd one out?

A **prohibited**

B **amusing**

C **legal**

D **lazy**

Which word means the same as LAWFUL?

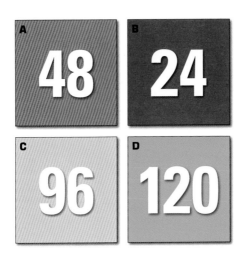

A 48

B 24

C 96

D 120

How many boxes measuring 0.5 x 1 x 1 metres can be packed into a container measuring 4 x 3 x 2 metres?

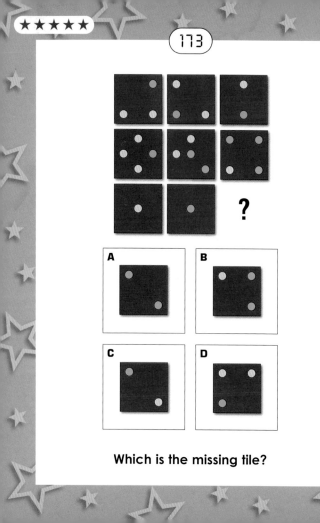

Which is the missing tile?

★★★★★

A that dream

B thread mat

C harmed mat

D heard Matt

Which of the above is NOT an
anagram of MAD HATTER?

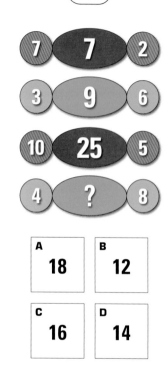

A	B
18	12

C	D
16	14

What number should replace the question mark?

★★★★★

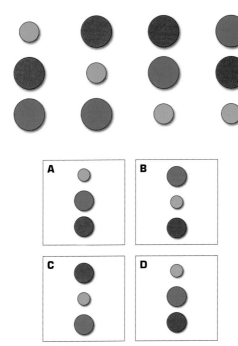

What comes next?

A Helium always heads for the sun

B Helium is lighter than air

C Helium always tries to escape the earth's atmosphere

D Helium propels them

Why do balloons filled with helium rise?

Friday 60°

Saturday 20°

A	B
10°	**30°**

C	D
40°	**20°**

The above are the night-time
temperatures for a region over two nights.
What is the average night-time
temperature over the two nights?

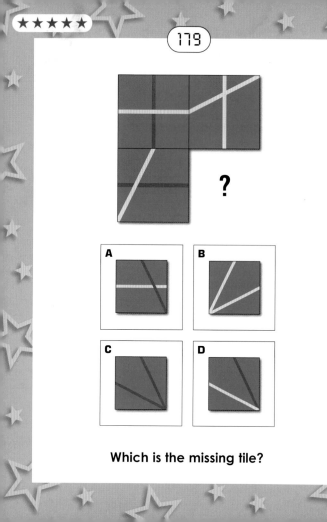

Which is the missing tile?

★★★★★

ABCDEFGH

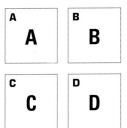

What letter comes two to the right of the
letter five to the left of the letter G?

9	2	18	6
7	3	21	7
12	2	24	8
6	7	42	?

A 9

B 14

C 18

D 16

What number should replace
the question mark?

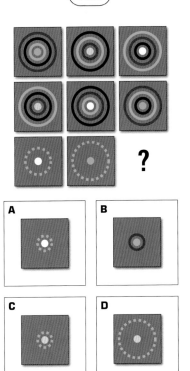

Which is the missing tile?

A old

B copy

C forgery

D correction

Which word means
the opposite of ORIGINAL?

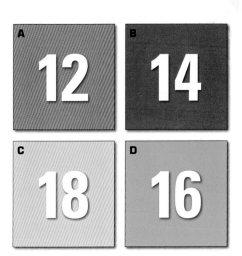

A 12

B 14

C 18

D 16

I collect 56 apples from my orchard. On my way home I first meet my brother and give him 12 apples. I then give 25% of the apples remaining to my son, then I eat one of the apples still remaining after that. Finally I give half of the apples remaining to my neighbor. How many apples do I arrive home with?

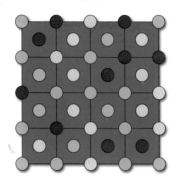

A

B

C

D

Which of the patterns above
appears in the grid?

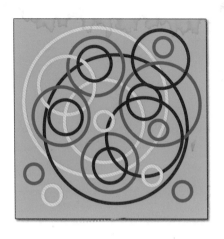

A	B
19	**23**

C	D
24	**21**

How many circles are there?

OTHER TITLES

There are many other exciting quiz
and puzzle books in the IntelliQuest range,
and your QUIZMO electronic unit
knows the answers to them all!

You can order from your local
IntelliQuest stockist or on-line bookseller.

For a full listing of current titles
(and ISBN numbers) see:

www.thelagoongroup.com/intelliquest

LAGOON
BOOKS